POKÉMON™

TRAINER'S DIARY

By Maria S. Barbo

SCHOLASTIC INC.

D0111874

ISBN 978-1-338-82934-1

10 9 8 7 6 5 4 3 2 1   22 23 24 25 26

Designed by Kay Petronio

Printed in China   68

First printing 2022

DRAW OR PASTE A PICTURE OF YOU AND YOUR POKÉMON HERE:

Name:

Age:

Height: tong

First Pokémon caught: pika chu

Years as a Pokémon Trainer: 10

Number of Pokémon caught: 6

ALL ABOUT ME

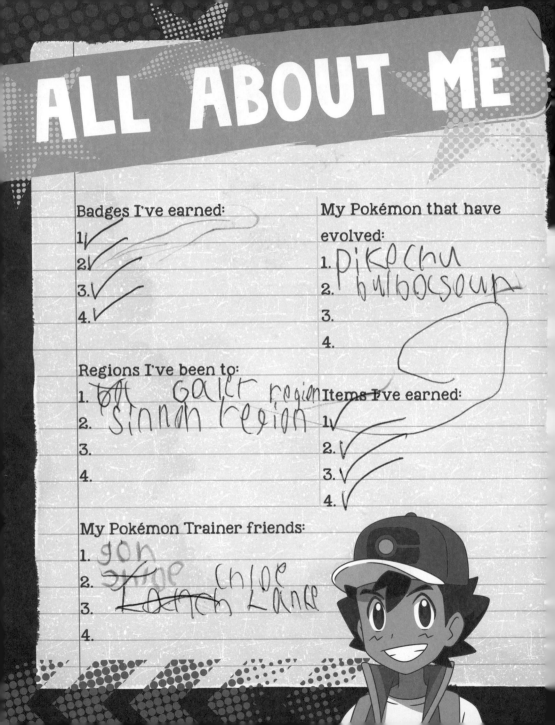

Badges I've earned:

1. ✓
2. ✓
3. ✓
4. ✓

Regions I've been to:

1. ~~Bo~~ galcr region
2. sinnoh region
3.
4.

My Pokémon Trainer friends:

1. gon
2. ~~chloe~~ chloe
3. ~~Kench~~ L'ance
4.

My Pokémon that have evolved:

1. Pikechu
2. bulboceoup
3.
4.

Items I've earned:

1. ✓
2. ✓
3. ✓
4. ✓

My Pokémon:

My funniest Pokémon: Impoleenp

My rarest Pokémon: Dragonite

My fiercest Pokémon: Venosour

My bravest Pokémon: Pikachu

My sweetest Pokémon:

My most unpredictable Pokémon:

My most evolved Pokémon:

Pick Your Pikachu!

Pokémon Trainer Ash Ketchum has had lots of adventures with his first partner Pokémon, Pikachu. Who do you choose as your best Pokémon buddy to join you on your journey through the Galar region?

CIRCLE YOUR GALAR REGION FIRST PARTNER POKÉMON:

SOBBLE	GROOKEY	SCORBUNNY
Type: Water	Type: Grass	Type: Fire

Now that you've chosen your Pokémon, what is the first thing you will do together? Draw or write about it here!

The Journey

Ash and Pikachu have a new plan—to see the world, one region at a time. And to start, they're heading to the Galar region!

Make a list of all the places you've been outside your hometown, then circle your favorite trip.

What did you love about it?

Make a list of all the places you want to go to this year, then circle your top choice.

Starts Today!

Why do you want to go there?

Now list everywhere you'd love to visit
in the world of Pokémon:

Where would you go first?

TIME TO TRADE!

What would you trade to get . . .

A Pikachu?

A Mew?

A Dragon-type Pokémon?

A Dynamax Band?

A Rotom Phone?

A chance to work with Professor Cerise?

A chance to go on a Pokémon journey with Ash, Goh, and Chloe?

A chance to battle Leon and his Charizard?

MAGICAL MEMORIES

Draw or write about your very first memory as a Pokémon Trainer. How does it make you feel to think about it?

WHO'S ON YOUR TEAM?

Draw all the Pokémon in your Poké Balls!

Pokémon name: Jigglypuff
Pokémon type: Phy

Best move:

Where I caught this
   Pokémon:

My favorite thing about
   this Pokémon:

Pokémon name:

Pokémon type:

Best move:

Where I caught this
   Pokémon:

My favorite thing about
   this Pokémon:

Pokémon name:

Pokémon type:

Best move:

Where I caught this
 Pokémon:

My favorite thing about
 this Pokémon:

Pokémon name:

Pokémon type:

Best move:

Where I caught this
 Pokémon:

My favorite thing about
 this Pokémon:

Pokémon name:

Pokémon type:

Best move:

Where I caught this
    Pokémon:

My favorite thing about
    this Pokémon:

Pokémon name:

Pokémon type:

Best move:

Where I caught this
    Pokémon:

My favorite thing about
    this Pokémon:

Pokémon name:

Pokémon type:

Best move:

Where I caught this
   Pokémon:

My favorite thing about
   this Pokémon:

Pokémon name:

Pokémon type:

Best move:

Where I caught this
   Pokémon:

My favorite thing about
   this Pokémon:

SQUAD GOALS

Now draw the top five Pokémon you're hoping to catch on your journey through the Galar region!

Pokémon name:

Pokémon type:

Best move:

My favorite thing about
    this Pokémon:

I want this Pokémon
    because:

Pokémon name:

Pokémon type:

Best move:

My favorite thing about
    this Pokémon:

I want this Pokémon
    because:

Pokémon name:

Pokémon type:

Best move:

My favorite thing about
this Pokémon:

I want this Pokémon
because:

Pokémon name:

Pokémon type:

Best move:

My favorite thing about
this Pokémon:

I want this Pokémon
because:

FIVE FAVES

Top Five Things I Like Most about My Pokémon:

1.

2.

3.

4.

5.

Top Five Things I Like Most about Myself:

1.

2.

3.

4.

5.

Top Five Things I Like Most
about the Galar Region:

1.

2.

3.

4.

5.

Top Five Things I Like Most about Ash and Pikachu:

1.

2.

3.

4.

5.

Top Five Things I Like Most about Goh and Scorbunny:

1.

2.

3.

4.

5.

My Best

Me vs. _____

Pokémon who battled:

Winning move:

Coolest moment:

What I learned:

Me vs. _____

Pokémon who battled:

Winning move:

Coolest moment:

What I learned:

Me vs. _____

Pokémon who battled:

Winning move:

Coolest moment:

What I learned:

Battles!

Me vs. _____

Pokémon who battled:

Winning move:

Coolest moment:

What I learned:

Me vs. _____

Pokémon who battled:

Winning move:

Coolest moment:

What I learned:

Me vs. _____

Pokémon who battled:

Winning move:

Coolest moment:

What I learned:

Now for a Twist!

Imagine you are having a Pokémon battle with Leon, winner of the World Coronation Series, and you can only use Pokémon you find in the Galar region.

Plan your strategy here! Keep in mind, Leon has a Gigantamax Charizard on his team!

MY TEAM OF POKÉMON:

	Name	Type
1.	sobie	water
2.	cinderace	fire
3.	charizard	fire
4.		
5.		

LEON'S POKÉMON:

	Name	Type
1.		
2.		
3.		
4.		
5.		

OUR MATCHUPS:

_____ vs. _____

_____ vs. _____

_____ vs. _____

_____ vs. _____

_____ vs. _____

Now imagine you are facing off against Team Rocket, and you can use any Pokémon EXCEPT Pikachu. Who do you choose?

Me vs. Team Rocket
OUR MATCHUPS:

Pikachu vs. Meowth

Cinderace vs. Chewtle

_____ vs. Wobbuffet

_____ vs. Morpeko

_____ vs. Ditto

FRESH START, FRESH FEELINGS!

How did you feel when you got your first partner Pokémon? Write or draw about it here.

How did you feel when you and your first partner Pokémon defeated another Pokémon in battle or caught your first Pokémon together? Write or draw about it here.

KNOW YOUR STRENGTHS

What are you good at? List your best traits here!

1.

2.

3.

4.

5.

List three things you've gotten better at this year.

1.

2.

3.

Now list three things you're still working on.

1.

2.

3.

Draw yourself feeling strong and confident!

GALAR GOALS

Ash wants to be a Pokémon Master. Goh wants to catch one of every type of Pokémon there is. And Chloe doesn't know what she wants!

What are your goals for today?

This week?

This year?

Don't know? That's A-OK! What's one thing you feel like doing right now?

When Ash decides he wants to battle Leon, the World Coronation Series Monarch, he knows he's going to have to get stronger by having lots of battles first.

Pick one of your goals from the previous page and break it down into smaller steps. Then write out your training plan here. What will you do to make it happen?

Dreaming of

In the Galar region, some Pokémon can supersize
themselves with the help of a Dynamax Band.

Have you ever wished you could Dynamax yourself
to deal with a challenge at school, to reach something
way up high, or to get a fresh perspective on things?
How would it help your situation? How might it make
everything even harder?

Dynamaxing?

Draw yourself Dynamaxed here!

GIGANTAMAX PROBLEMS

Some problems, fears, and feelings are SO big, they feel like an attack from a Gigantamax Pokémon. Think about a problem you're having a hard time solving. What would Ash tell you to do?

What would Ash's buddy Goh tell you to do?

What would Pikachu encourage you to do?

Now think about your own reaction. What does
your gut tell you to do?

FUNNY BUSINESS

What's the funniest thing that ever happened to you and your Pokémon? Draw or write about it here.

List the top three funniest Pokémon:

1.

2.

3.

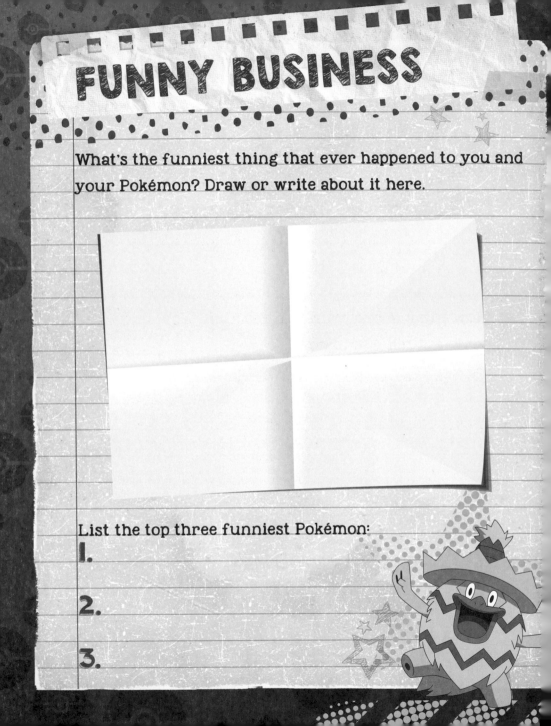

List three things that make you laugh out loud:

1.

2.

3.

What makes you and your Pokémon laugh harder than anything else? Why?

Draw or write about a time when you laughed so hard, everyone around you started laughing, too!

FIERY FEELINGS

Anger is an important emotion. At its best, it lets us know that something isn't right and spurs us to take action—like when Ash sees Team Rocket trying to steal a Pokémon. But sometimes anger feels awful—like a Thunderbolt from Pikachu.

Think about a time when your anger inspired you to take a stand for a friend or for a Pokémon. Write about it here.

Now think of a time when you felt angry and it didn't feel so good. Write about it here.

GIGANTAMAX CINDERACE

Watch out! Fireball incoming!

CINDERACE

You want to strike something hard and leave it scorched!

RABOOT

You are going to storm off for a while and no one can stop you!

SCORBUNNY

You may want to double-kick a tree but you'll get over it.

Why do you think you got so mad?

Is there something you can do differently if this happens again?

Now draw a picture of your first partner Pokémon defeating Scorbunny, Raboot, Cinderace, or Gigantamax Cinderace in a Pokémon battle. Feel any better?

GOTTA CATCH

How would you capture these wild Pokémon?

SCORBUNNY

I'd catch this Pokémon by:

RIOLU

I'd catch this Pokémon by:

MEW

I'd catch this Pokémon by:

GENGAR

I'd catch this Pokémon by:

FARFETCH'D

I'd catch this Pokémon by:

EEVEE

I'd catch this Pokémon by:

DRAGONITE

I'd catch this Pokémon by:

CHARIZARD

I'd catch this Pokémon by:

WOULD YOU RATHER . . . ?

Which option would you choose between each of these choices? Circle your answers, then describe why!

Get electro-shocked by a Yamper or bitten by a Chewtle?
Why?

Wake a sleeping Dynamax Snorlax or take a math test?
Why?

Have Pikachu or Scorbunny on your team?
Why?

Get pinched by a Pinsir or

never catch another Pokémon again?

Why?

Lose a Pokémon you are trying to catch or

lose your homework?

Why?

RATE YOUR DAY

Right now, I am feeling _____ sad _____ because:

I lost oncofmy poke mons

So, with my Pokémon ___ pikacu ___ I am going to:

I wish I had the moves of a ___ Fire ___ -type
Pokémon like ___ charmsnder ___ ,
so I could:

Right now, I am feeling _____ because:

So, with my Pokémon _____, I am going to:

Tomorrow will be even better / more challenging *(circle one)* because:

RATE YOUR WEEK

DAY
Monday
Tuesday
Wednesday
Thursday
Friday
Saturday
Sunday

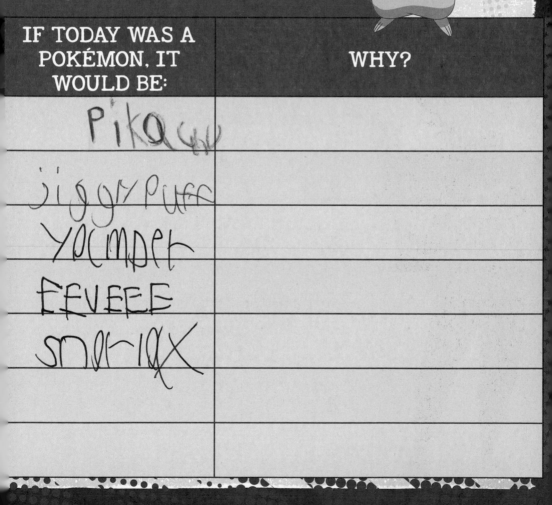

Keep track of how each day goes for you all week! Fill out the chart below:

IF TODAY WAS A POKÉMON, IT WOULD BE:	WHY?
Pikachu	
jigglypuff	
yvelmpet	
EEVEEE	
snorlax	

TWO OF A KIND

The two of you act exactly the same!

Goh was talking about Ash and Pikachu scarfing down scones in the Galar region, but it's true, people and their Pokémon have a lot in common. Sometimes they even look alike!

List the top three ways you and your favorite Pokémon are a lot alike.

1.

2.

3.

Now list three ways you and your favorite Pokémon are totally different.

1.

2.

3.

What is your favorite part of your friendship with your Pokémon? Draw or write about it here.

PHOTO OP

Draw or paste pics here of the coolest new Pokémon you've seen. Then list the top three things you've learned—or want to learn—about each of them!

Pokémon name: _____

_____

1. _____

2. _____

3. _____

Pokémon name:

_____

1. _____

2. _____

3. _____

Pokémon name:

_____

1. _____

2. _____

3. _____

TWO THINGS

Sometimes, you can have two opposite feelings at the same time. You can be happy you won a Gym battle and sad because your Pokémon got really tired in the process. (Like Ash!)

You can love your Raboot and feel like it's time to part ways. (Like Goh.)

You can love your Yamper but not be sure how you feel about being a Pokémon Trainer. (Like Chloe!)

Have you ever had a jumble of feelings so big and confusing you weren't sure exactly WHAT was going on? Scribble down all the different things you are feeling right now!

CAN BE TRUE!

MAKING THE BEST OF IT!

When Ash and Goh first arrived in the Galar region, they had to wait more than three hours to catch the next train to the Wild Area. So they decided to find some food, and they ended up meeting a really cool Scorbunny!

Think about a time when something you wanted to do didn't work out as you planned. How did it feel?

Now think of a time when things worked out even better because they didn't go how you thought they would. Draw or write about your feelings here!

Get up and Goh!

Some people, like Goh, have lots of energy in the morning. Some, like Ash, prefer to sleep in. Are you a morning person or a night owl?

What's your morning routine? Do you shower and have breakfast? Do you train with your Pokémon before school? Do you just grab an apple and run out the door?

Draw a picture of your Pokémon partner's favorite breakfast here.

berries

When you're feeling sleepier than a Snorlax during the day, what do you do when you need an energy boost?

WHO'S THAT POKÉMON?

Can you identify these Pokémon just by looking at details?

After you recognize them, write down everything you remember about them. Then circle your favorite Pokémon!

1.

Name: _Lucario_

Traits: _____

_____

2.

Name: _DreDnocw_

Traits: _____

_____

3.

Name: _Growlithe_

Traits: _____

_____

4.

Name: _____

Traits: _____

_____

5.

Name: SrYther

Traits: _____

_____

6.

Name: SYYi GY GYaraclos

Traits: _____

_____

7.

Name: charmander

Traits: _____

_____

_____

8.

Name: _____

Traits: _____

_____

LOVE IT? LIST IT!

Top Three Fiercest Pokémon:

1.

2.

3.

Top Three Coolest Pokémon Newly

Discovered in the Galar Region:

1.

2.

3.

Top Three Previously Discovered Pokémon:

1.

2.

3.

Top Three Cutest Pokémon:

1.

2.

3.

Top Three Most Loyal Pokémon:

1.

2.

3.

Top Three Pokémon Trainers:

1.

2.

3.

Top Three Best Things about
the Galar Region:

1.

2.

3.

TAG BATTLE TIME!

When Gigantamax Drednaw attacked the stadium after the World Coronation Series finals, Ash and Goh tag battled the Drednaw side by side. Which friend would you choose to help you save your school from a rampaging Gigantamax Pokémon attack? Why?

Which Pokémon would you choose to kick off the battle? Why?

Draw or write the story of your battle here.

PLAYTIME!

You can deepen your bonds with the Pokémon you catch by playing with them. What's your favorite way to spend a day with your Pokémon? Write and draw about it here!

WHO'S GOT YOUR BACK?

Good friends support each other, like Ash and Goh do when they are exploring, training, and battling their Pokémon.

List the top five traits of a great friend.

1.

2.

3.

4.

5.

List the top five traits of a great Pokémon.

1.

2.

3.

4.

5.

Now fill in this chart that's all about your friends!

MY CLOSEST FRIENDS	WHY WE'RE FRIENDS	THEIR FAVORITE POKÉMON

WHO'S GOT YOUR BACK? continued

Think of a time when one of your friends really supported you in something—at school, while playing, during a Pokémon battle, or elsewhere. Write or draw about it here.

What's one way *you* could help support one of your friends in something they're doing or trying to do? Write or draw about it here.

Sharing with friends is what it's all about!

ROCKY

Most friends have a fight once in a while. Think of a
time when you and your friend or Pokémon weren't
getting along.

How did it feel?

RELATIONSHIPS

What did you do to work it out?

What did you learn about what it takes to be a good friend?

MY FAVORITE TEACHERS

Along his journey, Ash learns a lot from teachers like Professor Oak, Professor Cerise, and Professor Magnolia.

My favorite teacher is _____

because _____.

If my favorite teacher had a Pokémon partner, it would

be _____, because _____

_____

_____.

The top five traits of a good teacher:

1. _____

2. _____

3. _____

4. _____

5. _____

Important things I've learned about life from my teachers:

Important things I've learned about Pokémon from others:

Draw a picture of your favorite teacher with their Pokémon partner here!

POKÉMON THAT MAKE ME FEEL . . .

Some Pokémon make you feel safe and loved and other Pokémon are just scary. Write about or draw the Pokémon that make you feel . . .

BRAVE

HAPPY

LOVED

SILLY

STRONG

ANXIOUS

CALM

AFRAID

READY FOR
ADVENTURE

READY FOR
A BATTLE

CHILL OUT!

Everyone gets nervous or anxious sometimes. Which of these options make you feel more anxious? Circle your answers for each.

Taking a test	OR	battling Pokémon?
Facing off against a Gym Leader	OR	facing off against Team Rocket?
Catching a Pokémon	OR	getting good grades?
Speaking in front of your whole class	OR	battling in a stadium?
Doing Pokémon research	OR	doing your homework?

What helps you relax when you are super stressed out?

List all the ways your Pokémon help you feel calm.

If your anxiety were a Pokémon, which Pokémon would it be?

Draw your favorite Pokémon blasting it with your best moves!

A LITTLE HELP FROM YOUR FRIENDS

When Ash battled a Gigantamax Centiskorch that was rampaging through a town, his first few moves didn't work at all. But did that stop Ash Ketchum? No way! Ash kept trying, and with some help from Leon, they were able to get the Centiskorch under control.

Write about something you were able to do with the help of your friends!

Who's That

Can you name all the Pokémon in this picture?

1._____

2._____

3._____

4._____

5._____

Pokémon?

Which one of these Pokémon would you most want to join your team, and why?

6._____

7._____

8._____

9._____

10._____

AWESOME . . . BUT AWKWARD

What is the MOST embarrassing thing that has ever happened to you? Write it in teeny-tiny letters here.

Now rewrite your story to be less embarrassing. Imagine that your favorite Pokémon were there to help rescue you!

TOTALLY AMAZING!

List the top ten things that amaze you about Pokémon:

1.

2.

3.

4.

5.

6.

7.

8.

9.

10.

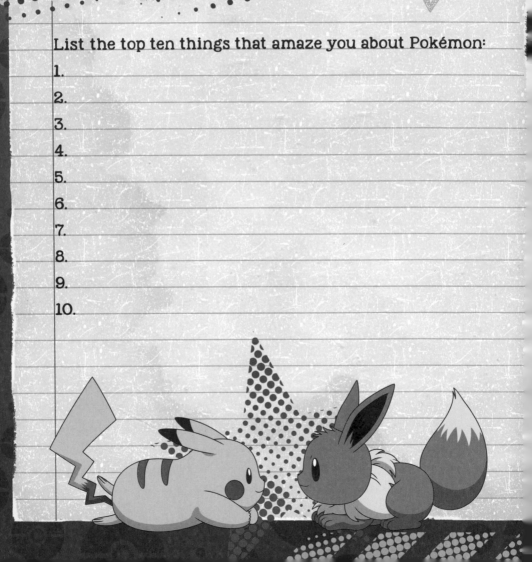

Now list the top ten things that amaze you about your friends:

1. _____

2. _____

3. _____

4. _____

5. _____

6. _____

7. _____

8. _____

9. _____

10. _____

ME TIME!

Most Pokémon like to rest inside their Poké Balls, but Pikachu's safe space is right on Ash's shoulder. Where do you go when you need some time to be alone? What makes it feel good?

Draw your favorite place here. How many Pokémon are there with you?

WILD AREA

All sorts of Pokémon can be found in the big open area of the Galar region known as the Wild Area. Goh once caught a slew of Bug-type Pokémon there. The Wild Area is also one of the few places outside a stadium where Pokémon can Dynamax.

Draw all the Pokémon you hope to find when you head into the wild. Are any of them Dynamaxing?

HAPPY DAYS!

Write everything that makes you happy all over this page. How many of them are about Pokémon?

What do you think would make these Pokémon happiest?

Pikachu is happiest when:

Snorlax is happiest when:

Togepi is happiest when:

Sobble is happiest when:

Bulbasaur is happiest when:

GIGANTAMAX YOUR GRATITUDE!

List the top ten things that make you most grateful for your Pokémon.

1.
2.
3.
4.
5.
6.
7.
8.
9.
10.

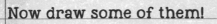

Now draw some of them!

YOU CAN'T WIN THEM ALL!

Ash's confidence gets shaken when he loses a battle with Bea. Then he loses three battles in a row, drops down a whole class in the World Coronation Series, and falls into a huge slump—until his friend Goh helps him out!

What would you say to a friend who was having a losing streak?

What do you wish someone would say to you when you are having a hard time?

GO ALL OUT!

Battles are no fun when you hold back because you don't feel confident. But they can feel awesome when you do your best—even if you don't win.

When I don't try my hardest, I feel:

When I go all out, I feel:

The things that make me feel most confident are:

WOULD YOU RATHER . . . ?

Which option would you choose between each of these choices? Circle your answers, then describe why!

Defeat Team Rocket or join Team Rocket?
Why?

Get stung by a Beedrill or not see your friends for two weeks?
Why?

Dynamax your Pokémon in a stadium or Gigantamax your Pokémon in the Wild Area?
Why?

Have Grookey or
Bulbasaur on your team?
Why?

Catch a cold or fail to catch a Gyarados?
Why?

WHAT WOULD A POKÉMON CHAMPION DO?

List the traits you think a Trainer needs to become a Pokémon Champion:

1.

2.

3.

Now imagine what a Pokémon Champion would do if . . .

A Dynamax Pokémon were rampaging through their town?

Team Rocket tried to steal a pack of Pikachu?

Professor Cerise offered them a job as a research fellow?

They saw someone at school picking on another Pokémon Trainer?

They lost the World Coronation Series finals?

They found a Pokémon fossil?

Pokémon

Were battling in the World Coronation Series championship?

Pokémon name: charmander

Type: fire

Best moves: fire blast

Why I chose this Pokémon:

Were battling Team Rocket?

Pokémon name: dragonite

Type: dragon H

Best moves:

Why I chose this Pokémon:

Dream Team

Had to do a lot of chores that you didn't want to do?

Pokémon name:

Type:

Best moves:

Why I chose this Pokémon:

Had to speak in front of your whole class?

Pokémon name:

Type:

Best moves:

Why I chose this Pokémon:

Had to save an entire town from a rampaging Gigantamax Coalossal?

Pokémon name:

Type:

Best moves:

Why I chose this Pokémon:

WHAT DO YOU THINK?

Which of each of these options do you think is better? Circle your answers!

BEST TYPE

Fire or Electric?

Water or Grass?

Dragon or Ghost?

Normal or Ground?

Dark or Rock?

BEST MOVE

Flamethrower or Dragon Dance?

Ice Fang or Thunder Punch?

Electroweb or Thunderbolt?

Double Kick or Quick Attack?

G-Max Wildfire or G-Max Stonesurge?

BEST TRAINER

Goh or Ash?

Jessie or James?

Chloe or Iris?

Lance or Leon?

Professor Oak or
   Professor Cerise?

BEST FIRST
PARTNER POKÉMON

Scorbunny or Sobble?

Grookey or Pikachu?

Pikachu or Scorbunny?

Sobble or Grookey?

BEST REGION

Galar or Johto?

Sinnoh or Hoenn?

Alola or Unova?

Kalos or Kanto?

Sinnoh or Alola?

Kanto or Galar?

BEST LEGENDARY
AND MYTHICAL
POKÉMON

Zacian or Zamazenta?

Mew or Lugia?

Galarian Zapdos or
   Galarian Articuno?

Eternatus or Zarude?

TEAM-UP TUESDAY

Teamwork makes the dream work. Ash loves to work together with his Pokémon to help others. This month, team up with someone every Tuesday to volunteer or do community service.

TUESDAY #1:

I teamed up with:

Our project:

How we helped:

TUESDAY #2:

I teamed up with:

Our project:

How we helped:

TUESDAY #3:

I teamed up with:

Our project:

How we helped:

TUESDAY #4:

I teamed up with:

Our project:

How we helped:

STRATEGY SESSION

Finding and catching Pokémon isn't easy. If a Pokémon doesn't want to be caught, it will fight back, and if you make a big scene, the Pokémon may run away. No matter what, you've got to stay calm, and you might not want to try to catch it right away.

What are your strategies for catching Pokémon?

What's the most fun you've ever had catching a
Pokémon? Write the story here.

EVEN PIKACHU FEELS LEFT OUT SOMETIMES!

When Ash starts training his Riolu, Pikachu feels so left out and jealous that it runs back home to Pallet Town. Think of a time when you were left out of something you really wanted to do. How did it feel?

How does it feel to know that even Pikachu feels left out and lonely sometimes?

Confession session: Have you ever left someone out of an activity or hangout? What was your reason?

PICTURE THIS!

Draw a picture of some defining moments with your Pokémon!

Our scariest moment:

Our happiest moment:

Our most
stressful
moment:

Our most chill
moment:

WHO'S THAT POKÉMON?

After you recognize them, write down everything you remember about them. Then circle your favorite Pokémon!

1.

Name: _____

Traits: _____

_____

2.

Name: _____

Traits: _____

_____

3.

Name: _____

Traits: _____

_____

4.

Name: _____

Traits: _____

_____

5.

Name: _____

Traits: _____

_____

6.

Name: _____

Traits: _____

_____

7.

Name: _____

Traits: _____

_____

8.

Name: _____

Traits: _____

_____

THE FUTURE IS IN THE PALM OF YOUR HAND

Goh knows his future will be filled with lots of Pokémon.

What do you think tomorrow will be like for you?

What about your birthday or the day you catch your 100th Pokémon? How will you celebrate?

Follow Your

Pokémon are teeming with mystery! Professor Cerise opened up a whole research facility in Vermilion City dedicated to uncovering the mysteries of Pokémon in every region.

Team Rocket wants to catch—or steal—Pikachu, so they do everything they can think of to learn more about it, including sending out a drone to record Pikachu's every move and facing off against Pikachu in battle.

What is something you are super curious about?

Why do you find it so interesting?

Curiosity!

List three things you can do to learn more about it!

1.

2.

3.

Now list three things you were surprised to learn about Pokémon.

1.

2.

3.

ALL THE FEELS!

Draw or describe how you feel . . .

When you and your
friends trade Pokémon:

When you spot a
Legendary Pokémon:

When you lose a
Pokémon battle:

When Team Rocket goes
blasting off again:

When your
teacher talks about
Pokémon during
school:

When your best
friend decides
to join you on
your Pokémon
journey:

ALL THE FEELS!
continued

When your
Pokémon won't do
what you ask:

When you watch
a Pokémon
Gigantamax:

When your
Pokémon gets hurt
during a battle:

When a
Pokémon asks
to join your
team:

When the
Pokémon you
REALLY want
to catch gets
away:

When you make
a new friend
who also loves
Pokémon:

IN OVER YOUR HEAD

Write down how you feel when someone tells you, "Don't try it. You're in over your head."

How do you think Ash would respond if another Trainer told him a Pokémon battle was so hard he shouldn't even try it?

Give It Everything You've Got!

What do you love? What do you work hardest at? What do you want to get really good at?

Draw a picture of you and your Pokémon putting in 100 percent effort to achieve your goals.

POKÉMON HANGOUT

Do you have friends who are also into Pokémon? What are some of your favorite things to do when you are all together? Write and draw about it here!

FEELINGS OF ALL SIZES

Sometimes Pokémon and people feel small,
and sometimes they feel enormous—and not just
because of their physical size.

On a scale from Milcery to Steelix, how big are you
feeling today?

Mark the spot. How would you describe the size?

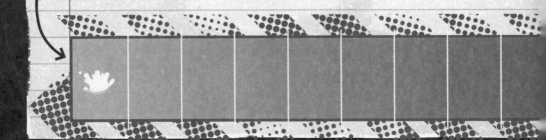

Now get curious. What made you feel that way?

THE JOURNEY CONTINUES!

What's your plan for your next adventure with your Pokémon?

Draw a picture of you and all your Pokémon heading out together!